Look what's FREE for your 4 to 8 year old from

DISNEY's WONDERFUL WORLD OF READING

...not you buy any books!

See the other side for details . . .

WALT DISNEY'S

Winnie the Pooh and Tigger too

©MCMLXXVI Walt Disney Productions

WINNIE THE POOH AND TIGGER TOO

Your child meets Winnie the Pooh and all his friends — Piglet, Rabbit, Kanga and Roo — in this delightful book. And joins them as they try to teach that bouncy Tigger *not* to bounce! But the lesson turns out to be full of surprises for everybody — and the story's sure to be a favorite!

YOURS FREE

with no obligation to buy any books!

If reply cards are missing, write to: **Dept. WB**
DISNEY'S WONDERFUL WORLD OF READING
Sherman Turnpike, Danbury, Conn. 06816

Get your order card on next page

Presenting... Disney's
WONDERFUL WORLD OF READING

The magic of DISNEY in all-new easy-to-read books created exclusively for this book club!

TAKE DISNEY'S WINNIE THE POOH AND TIGGER TOO FREE just for looking at **3 OTHER DISNEY BOOKS** — all yours to keep for only **$1.95** (a $10.00 value)

Good Housekeeping — A LIMITED WARRANTY TO CONSUMERS — PROMISES — REPLACEMENT OR REFUND IF DEFECTIVE

©MCMLXXVI Walt Disney Productions

What a wonderful idea! Why shouldn't your child's favorite Disney pals be the ones to help him take a giant step into the WONDERFUL WORLD OF READING? That's why Walt Disney Productions and Random House, leading publisher of quality children's books, have created this fabulous program of colorful, easy-to-read books.

America's favorite book club for children 4 to 8

DISNEY'S WONDERFUL WORLD OF READING already serves more than 500,000 happy children! Shouldn't your favorite 4 to 8 year old join the fun? All the famous Disney characters are here: Cinderella, Dumbo, Pinocchio, Donald Duck, Mickey Mouse, Bambi, Thumper, Peter Pan, Snow White . . . many more!

To introduce you to this exciting book club, we'd like to send your child a copy of Disney's WINNIE THE POOH AND TIGGER TOO to keep FREE, plus the 3 introductory books to try (total publisher's value $11.80). If you keep the 3 introductory books for only $1.95 plus delivery, each month thereafter, your child will receive an all-new, easy-to-read Disney book!

But you need not keep even one additional book, because you may cancel your child's membership *at any time*. For each book you keep, you'll be billed only $2.25 plus delivery — and continue to save on the retail price of $2.95 per book.

Send for your FREE BOOK now — plus 3 others to try without risk!

Use a tear-out order form now to send for your child's FREE copy of Disney's WINNIE THE POOH AND TIGGER TOO plus 3 introductory books to try free for 14 days. You've nothing to lose — and your child has everything to gain! So fill out and mail an order form today!

"My four year old daughter is able to 'read' them herself!"
"I'd like to tell you of my surprise at finding my four year old daughter actually reading one of your books aloud the other day. She loves the books!"
Robert R. Bauer
Keene, New Hampshire

". . . he takes his *Bambi* to bed with him!"
"By the way, my son loves your books. He is only three years old but he enjoys my reading to him and he takes his *Bambi* to bed with him!"
Mrs. Robert F. Lozano
South Gate, California

". . . she can recite every book almost word for word."
"The enjoyment that our four year old daughter receives from the books is something you can't put a price tag on. Even though she doesn't read yet, she can recite every book almost word for word!"
Mrs. Jan McUlane
Hemet, California

". . . a few words of thanks for my five year old Wendy."
"She truly enjoys the books . . . and is looking forward to new books which we will share with her. Thank you again!"
Mrs. Emily Kreitlow
for Wendy Kreitlow
Wall Lake, Iowa

grolier

NNIE THE POOH AND TIGGER TOO

BEE TREE

BIG
STONES
AND
ROX

MY HOUSE

HOLLOW LOG

TIGGER

WALT DISNEY'S

Winnie the Pooh

Published by permission of E.P. Dutton & Co., Inc., the publishers of WINNIE-THE-POOH (Copyright, 1926, by E.P. Dutton & Co., Inc. Copyright Renewal, 1954, by A.A. Milne), THE HOUSE AT POOH CORNER (Copyright, 1928, by E.P. Dutton & Co., Inc. Copyright Renewal, 1956, by A.A. Milne), WHEN WE WERE VERY YOUNG (Copyright, 1924, by E.P. Dutton & Co., Inc. Copyright Renewal, 1952, by A.A. Milne), and NOW WE ARE SIX (Copyright, 1927, by E.P. Dutton & Co., Inc. Copyright Renewal, 1955, by A.A. Milne).

Library of Congress Cataloging in Publication Data
Main entry under title: Walt Disney's Winnie the Pooh and Tigger too. (Disney's Wonderful World of Reading, #35) Based on stories written by A.A. Milne. Rabbit plans to unbounce Tigger, but he discovers he likes a bouncy Tigger best. [1. Friendship—Fiction] I. Milne, Alan Alexander, 1882-1956. II. Disney (Walt) Productions III. Title: Winnie the Pooh and Tigger too. PZ7.W168977 [E] 75-20349
ISBN 0-394-82569-1   ISBN 0-394-92569-6 (lib. bdg.)   1 2 3 4 5 6 7 8 9 0
Manufactured in the United States of America.
C D E F G H I J K
6 7 8

and Tigger too

Random House 🏠 New York

One morning Winnie-the-Pooh was
on his way to visit his friend Piglet.
Although Pooh's head was stuffed
with fluff, he was a cheerful fellow.
As he walked along through the woods,
he was humming a song to himself.

Pooh did not look where he was going.
All of a sudden—
someone bounced into him.

Pooh found himself flat on the ground.
Tigger was sitting on his tummy.
"Hello, Pooh," said Tigger.
"It's a fine day for bouncing."

Tigger helped Pooh get up.

"Thank you, Tigger," said Pooh.
"I was just thinking it's a fine day
for going to visit Piglet."

"I was on my way to see Rabbit,"
said Tigger. "But I will come
along with you."

And Tigger bounced away.

Tigger bounced on ahead of Pooh.
He bounced so fast . . .

and he bounced so far . . .

that he bounced right into Piglet.

"Tigger," cried Piglet. "You scared me."
"I'm sorry," said Tigger.
He helped Piglet get up.

"Now I'm off to see Rabbit," said Tigger.
"Why don't you and Pooh come with me?"
Away he bounced again.

Tigger bounced into Rabbit's garden.
Rabbit was busy counting his carrots.

Suddenly Tigger bounced on top of him.
"Hello there, Rabbit," said Tigger.
"Tigger, you're a pest!" cried Rabbit.

When Pooh and Piglet reached the garden,
they helped Rabbit to his feet.

Rabbit was very angry at Tigger.

"Why are you always so bouncy?" he cried.

"Bouncing is what I do best!" Tigger said,
and he began to sing:

The wonderful thing about Tiggers is—
Tiggers are wonderful things.
Their tops are made of rubber.
Their tails are made of springs.

They're bouncy, trouncy, flouncy, pouncy.
Full of fun, fun, fun!
The most wonderful thing about Tiggers is—
I'm the only one!

By the time Tigger bounced away,
Rabbit's whole garden was ruined.

Later that day, Rabbit came up with
a splendid idea for UNBOUNCING Tigger.

He told Pooh and Piglet about it.
"We will take him on a long explore,
and leave him in the woods," said Rabbit.
"When we go back to get him next morning,
Tigger will not be so bouncy."

"That is a splendid idea," said Piglet.
"What do you think, Pooh?"

But Pooh was sitting in a cozy chair
and he had fallen fast asleep.

Piglet poked him.
"I think it's
a splendid idea,"
said Pooh after
Piglet told him
all about it.

The very next day Rabbit, Pooh, and Piglet
took Tigger into the woods.

"When we come back to get Tigger tomorrow,"
said Rabbit, "the bounces will all be gone.
He'll be a sad Tigger! A sorry Tigger!
A Rabbit-I'm-so-glad-to-see-you Tigger!"

Tigger bounced farther and farther away.
He did not know about Rabbit's idea
to leave him in the woods.

The three friends found a hollow log.
"Quick!" said Rabbit. "Hide inside!"
They climbed into the log.

Tigger soon came back to look for them.
"Hello-o-o-o," he called.
No one answered.

Tigger stood on top of the log.
He called to his friends again.
They still did not answer.

"They must be lost," thought Tigger.
And he bounced away to find them.

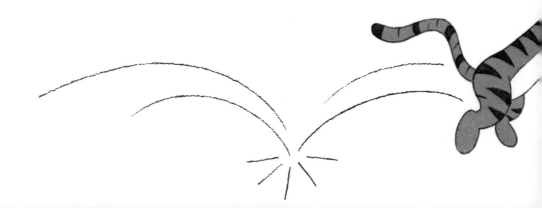

As soon as Tigger was out of sight,
Rabbit, Pooh, and Piglet started home.
After a while they came to a sandpit.
"Something is wrong," said Piglet.
"I'm sure we passed by here before."
"Nonsense," said Rabbit. "Keep walking."

Soon they came to the sandpit again.
"I believe we're lost," said Pooh.
"We have been looking for home, but
we keep finding this sandpit. Maybe
if we start looking for this sandpit,
we will find our way home."

"I'm sure I know the way," said Rabbit.
"You two wait here and I'll find it."

Pooh and Piglet waited for Rabbit.
They waited...

and waited...

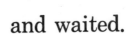

and waited.

But Rabbit did not come back.

At last Pooh took Piglet's hand.
"Let's follow my tummy," said Pooh.
"Whenever I get hungry for honey,
my tummy leads me home."

Sure enough, Pooh's tummy found the way.
Just as they came out of the woods
Tigger bounced into them.

"Oh, Tigger," said Pooh.
"Rabbit is lost in the woods."

"Tiggers never get lost," said Tigger.
"I'll go back to find him."
He bounced away.

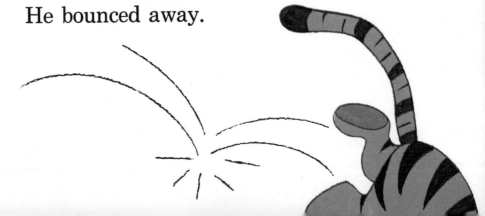

Meanwhile Rabbit was all alone
in the darkest part of the woods.
He was very, very lost.
Every time he looked around, he thought
he saw someone watching him.
He heard all sorts of scary sounds.

HOOT!

CHOMP!

Then Rabbit heard
someone creeping
in the bushes.
"Help, Pooh!
Help, Piglet!"
he shouted.

Suddenly he was bounced to the ground.
"Tigger!" Rabbit cried.
"I am so glad to see you!"

Tigger led Rabbit out of the woods.
Poor Rabbit! His splendid idea
for unbouncing Tigger had not
worked out very well.

Bright and early the very next morning
Tigger went to Kanga's house.

Kanga was busily sweeping the yard.

"May I take Roo for a walk with me?"
asked Tigger.

"Of course, dear," said Kanga.

As Tigger bounced along, Roo rode
on his back.

"Can Tiggers climb trees?" asked Roo.

"That's what Tiggers do best,"
said Tigger. "I will show you."

Tigger found a tall tree
and he bounced from
branch to branch.

He bounced up...
"Oo-o-o-o, Tigger!"
squealed Roo.

He bounced higher...

"Oo-o-o-o, Tigger!"
Roo squealed again.

He kept bouncing higher
and higher.
Soon they were near
the top of the tree.

When Tigger looked down
he was very scared.
"How did this tree
get so high?" he cried.
"Isn't it fun?" said Roo.
"No!" answered Tigger.
"I forgot to tell you.
Tiggers can't climb down!"
"Hooray!" squealed Roo.
"We'll stay here forever!"

Just at that moment Pooh and Piglet came by.
They happened to look up at the tree.

"Piglet," whispered Pooh. "There's a *jag-u-lar!*"

"Are *jagulars* fierce animals?" cried Piglet.

"I'm not really sure," said Pooh.

"Let's walk a bit closer and see."

When Pooh and Piglet
reached the tree, they saw
Tigger and Roo near the top.
"Hello-o-o!" called Roo.
"Tigger is stuck!"

"Don't worry, Tigger,"
called Pooh. "We will get
Christopher Robin. He'll think
of a way to rescue you."

Before long Christopher Robin appeared.
He ran to the tree with Rabbit and Kanga.
"I do hope Tigger has learned his lesson,"
said Rabbit. "Maybe he'll stop bouncing now!"

Christopher Robin took off his coat.
He told everyone to hold onto a corner
so Roo could jump into it.

After Roo came tumbling down,
Christopher Robin called up to Tigger.

"Now it's your turn to jump," he said.

"Tiggers don't jump, they bounce,"
said Tigger. "But if I ever get down from
here, I promise never to bounce again!"

"Did you all hear that?" cried Rabbit.
"He promised to stop bouncing!"

Tigger closed his eyes and let go of the tree.
Down...down...down he fell.

He landed on the coat with such a thump
that everyone fell backward.
Tigger was happy to be down.
He started to bounce.

But Rabbit held up his hand.
"No bouncing, Tigger," he said.
"You promised never to bounce again."
"That's right," said Tigger. "I did."

Tigger began to walk away.
Without his bounces he was
a very sad Tigger indeed.

Roo watched his unhappy friend.

"I like the old bouncy Tigger better," he said.

"So do I, dear," said Kanga.

"So do I," said Pooh and Piglet.

Everyone looked at Rabbit.

"Well," said Rabbit.

"So do I...

I guess."

All of a sudden Tigger came bouncing back.
"Do you really mean it, Rabbit?" he cried.
"May I have my bounces back?"
"Yes," said Rabbit. "I really mean it."

"Hooray!" said Tigger.
And off he bounced—happy
to be his bouncy old self again.